EASIEST 5-FI PIANO COLLE

C000192620

Huge Chart Hits

15 popular chart hits arranged for 5-finger piano

Wise Publications
part of The Music Sales Group
London / New York / Paris / Sydney / Copenhagen / Berlin / Madrid / Hong Kong / Tokyo

NIGHT CHANGES (One Direction)

Words & Music by John Ryan, Jamie Scott, Julian Bunetta, Harry Styles, Niall Horan, Liam Payne, Zain Malik & Louis Tomlinson

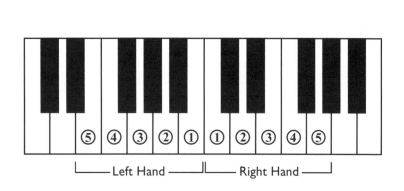

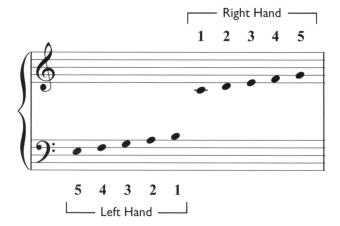

We're on-ly get-ting___ old-er, ba — by,

and I've been think-ing a-bout it late-ly;

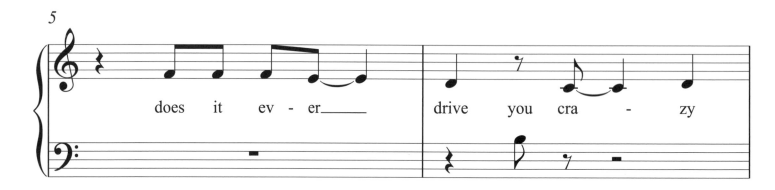

does it ev-er___ drive you cra — zy

WILDEST DREAMS (Taylor Swift)

Words & Music by Taylor Swift, Shellback & Max Martin

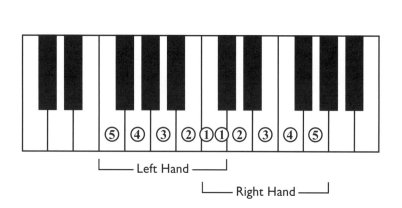

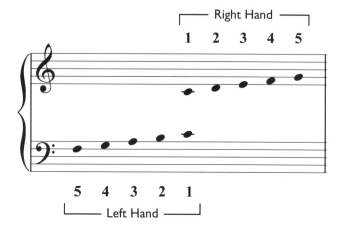

Expressively ♩ = 132

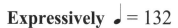

Say you'll re-mem-ber me standing in a

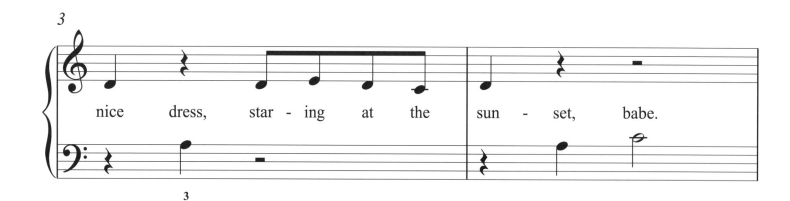

nice dress, star-ing at the sun-set, babe.

Red lips and ro - sy cheeks, say you'll see me

I'M NOT THE ONLY ONE (Sam Smith)

Words & Music by James Napier & Sam Smith

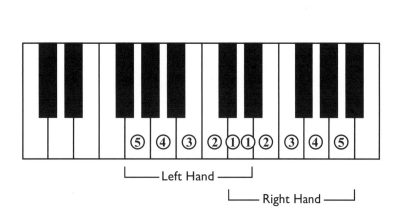

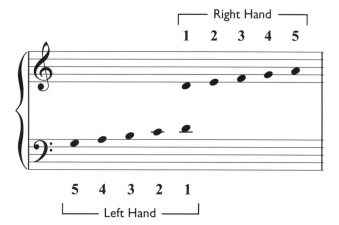

Leisurely ♩ = 84

You and me, we made a vow,

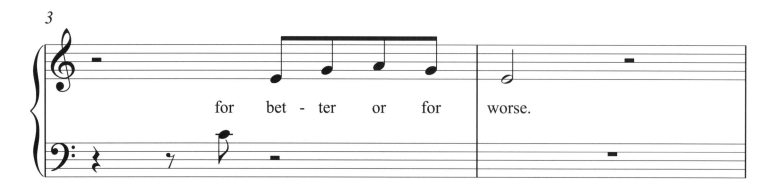

for bet- ter or for worse.

I can't be - lieve you let me down, but the

proof's in the way it___ hurts.___ You say I'm

cra - zy 'cause you don't think I know what you've done.___

___ But when you call me 'ba - by',___ I

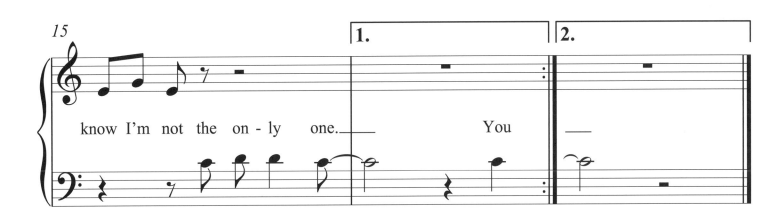

know I'm not the on - ly one.___ You

REAL LOVE (Tom Odell)

Words & Music by John Lennon
© *Copyright 1988 & 1995 Lenono Music.*
All Rights Reserved. International Copyright Secured.

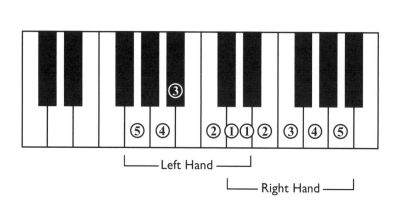

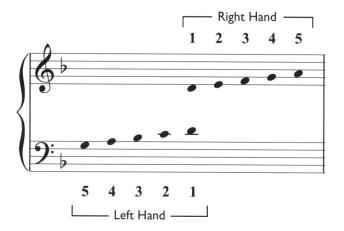

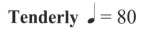

Tenderly ♩ = 80

All my lit - tle plans and schemes,

lost like some for - got - ten dream.

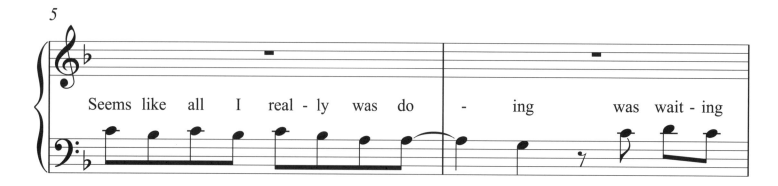

Seems like all I real - ly was do - ing was wait - ing

for you._____ Don't need to be____ a - lone,___

__ don't need to be____ a - lone.___

It's real_____ love,___ it's real,_____

it's real_____ love,___ it's real_____ love.

BLAME IT ON ME (George Ezra)

Words & Music by Joel Pott & George Ezra Barnett

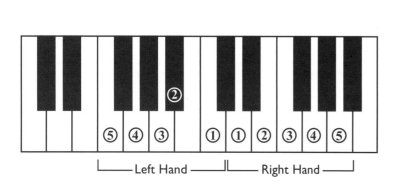

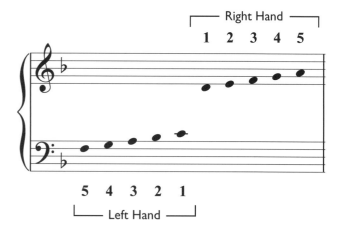

Sprightly ♩ = 96

The gar - den was blessed by the

gods of me and you.   We head - ed west for to

find our - selves some truth, oh.   What you wait - ing

JEALOUS (Labrinth)

Words & Music by Timothy McKenzie, Josh Kear & Natalie Hemby

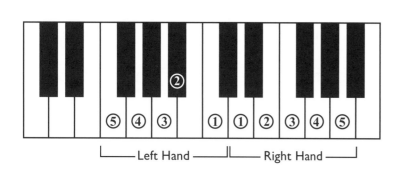

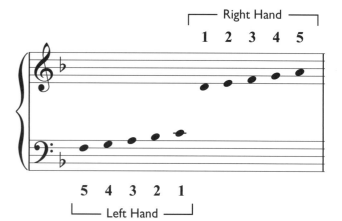

Steadily ♩ = 88

I'm jea - lous of the rain

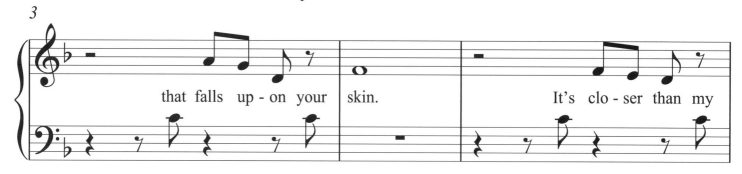

that falls up - on your skin. It's clo - ser than my

hands have been. I'm jea - lous of the rain.

'Cause I wished you___ the best of___

NEVER BEEN BETTER (Olly Murs)

Words & Music by Wayne Hector, Olly Murs, Thomas Barnes, Peter Kelleher & Benjamin Kohn

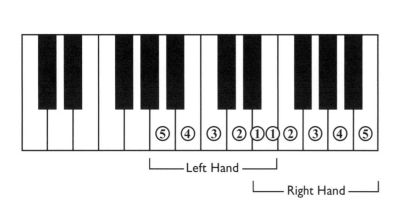

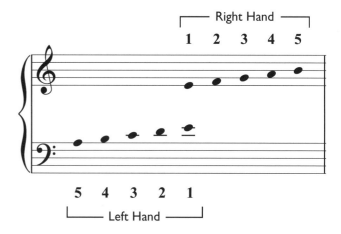

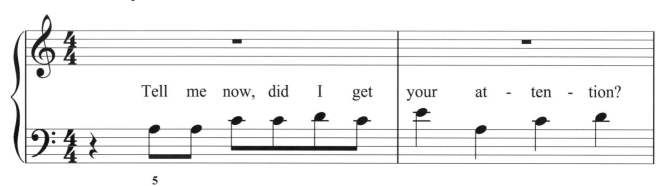

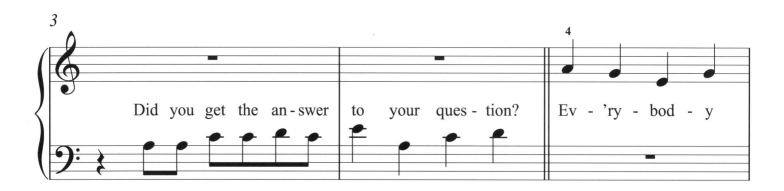

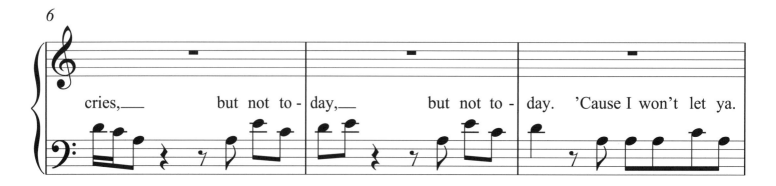

HOLD BACK THE RIVER (James Bay)

Words & Music by Iain Archer & James Bay

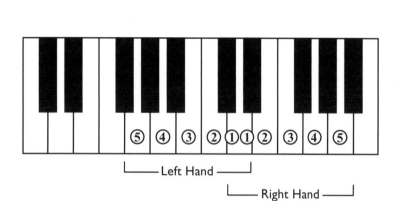

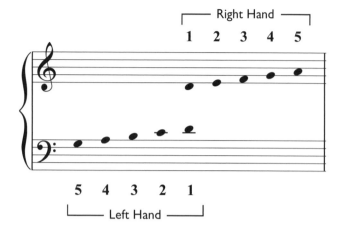

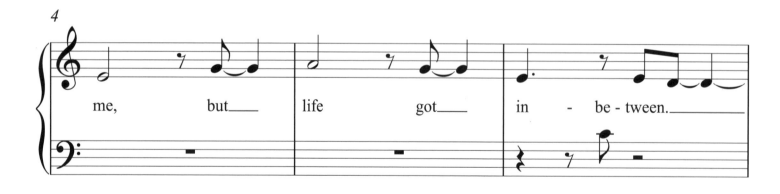

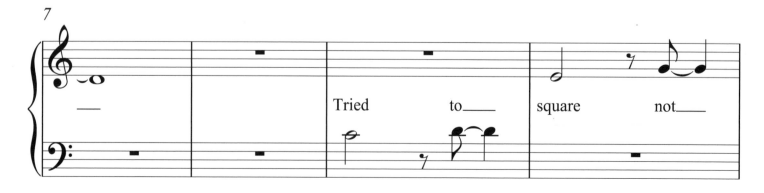

RUDE (Magic!)

Words & Music by Nasri Atweh, Adam Messinger, Ben Spivak, Mark Pellizzer & Alexander Tanasijczuk

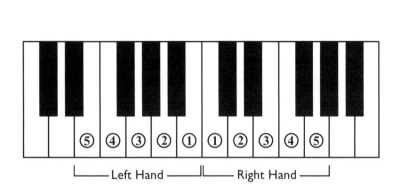

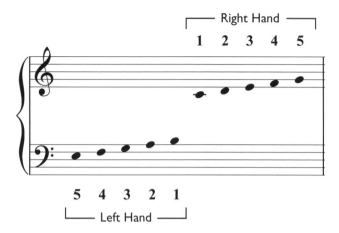

Spikily ♩ = 132

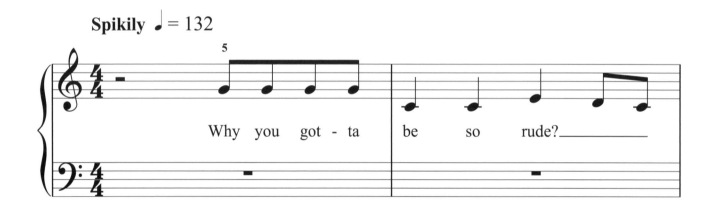

Why you got - ta be so rude?

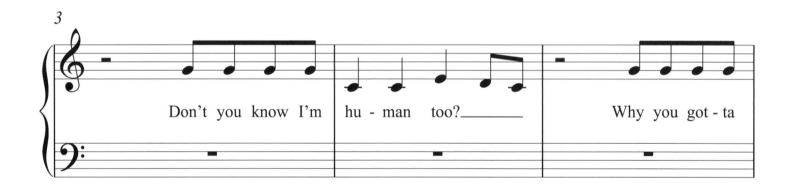

Don't you know I'm hu - man too? Why you got - ta

be so rude? I'm gon - na mar - ry her an - y - way.

1

GHOST (Ella Henderson)

Words & Music by Ryan Tedder, Noel Zancanella & Ella Henderson

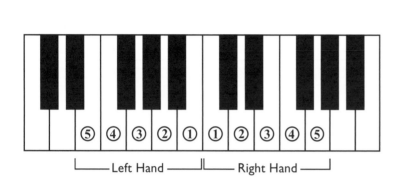

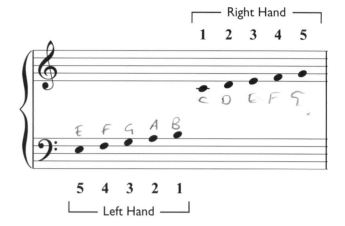

Lightly, with a bounce ♩ = 100

SHAKE IT OFF (Taylor Swift)

Words & Music by Max Martin, Taylor Swift & Shellback

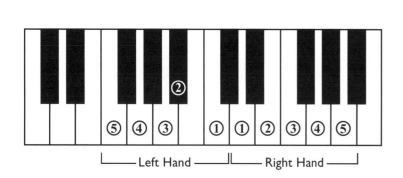

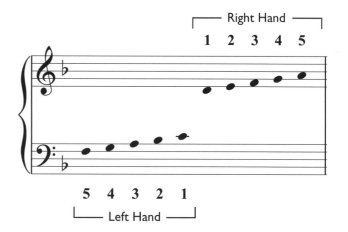

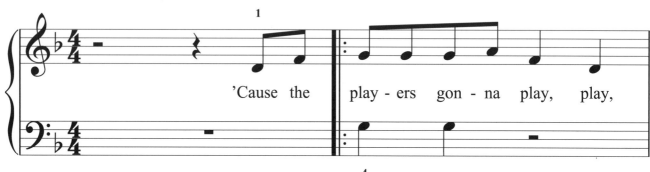

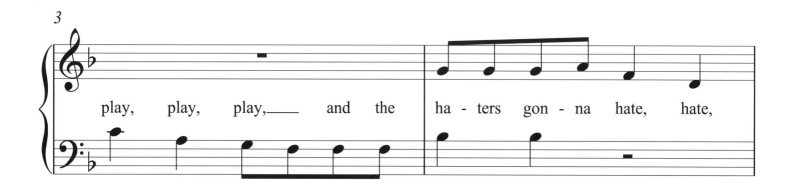

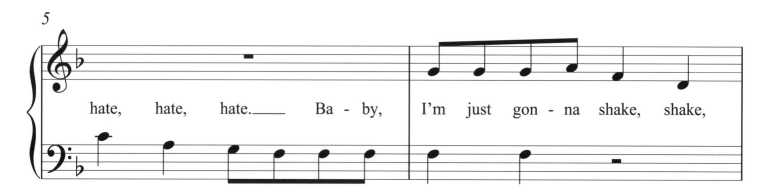

THINKING OUT LOUD (Ed Sheeran)

Words & Music by Ed Sheeran & Amy Wadge

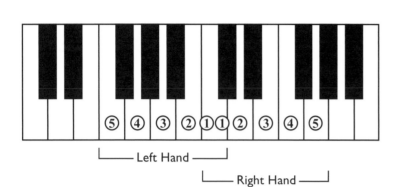

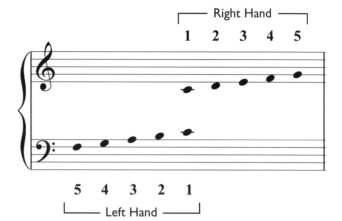

Thoughtfully ♩ = 76

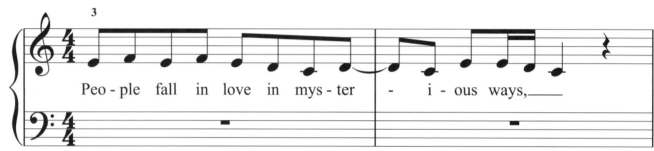

Peo-ple fall in love in mys-ter - i-ous ways,

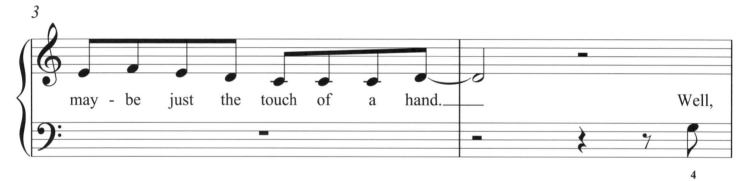

may-be just the touch of a hand. Well,

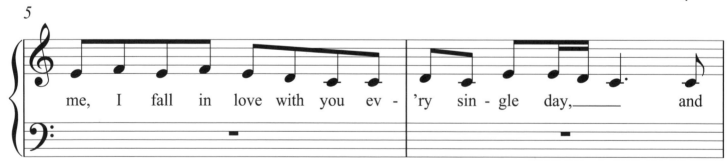

me, I fall in love with you ev-'ry sin-gle day, and

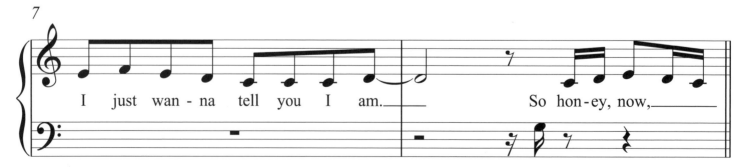

I just wan-na tell you I am. So hon-ey, now,

YOU GOT IT ALL (Union J)

Words & Music by Nasri Atweh & Greg Pegani

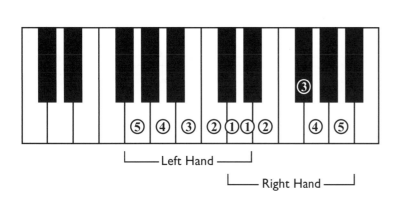

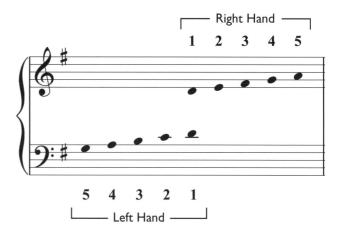

Passionately ♩ = 92

Some peo-ple got drive, some peo-ple got

tal - ent,___ some peo-ple got style,___ but you got it all.

Some peo-ple live life,___ some peo-ple stay

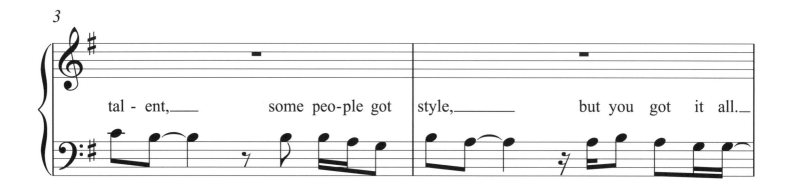

NO GOOD IN GOODBYE (The Script)

Words & Music by Mark Sheehan, Daniel O'Donoghue & James Barry

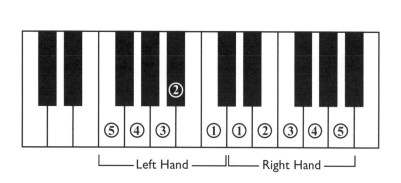

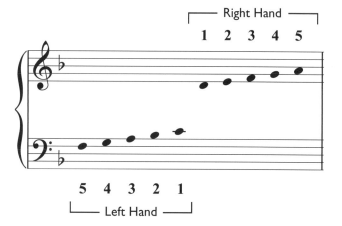

Where's the good___ in 'good - bye'?___ Where's the nice___ in 'nice try'?

Where's the us___ in 'trust' gone? Where's the soul___ in 'sol - dier

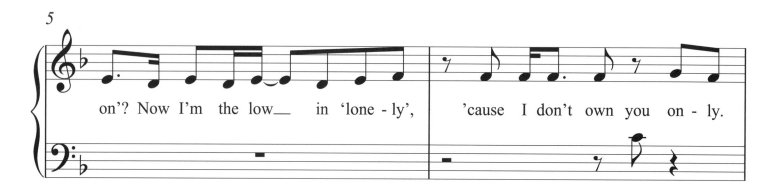

on'? Now I'm the low___ in 'lone - ly', 'cause I don't own you on - ly.

THESE DAYS (Take That)

Words & Music by Mark Owen, Gary Barlow, Howard Donald, Jamie Norton & Benjamin Weaver

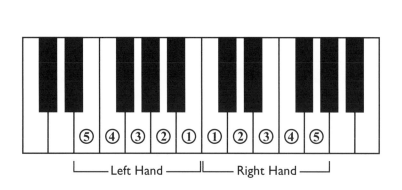

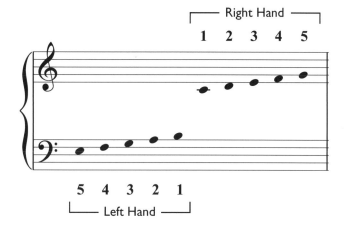

Rhythmically, with energy ♩ = 104

Take me___ back___ be - fore we all ex - plode,___ be - fore we

turn to___ stone,___ be - fore the light is___ gone.___

Take me___ back___ to where it all be - gan,___ to where our

3456789

EASIEST 5-FINGER PIANO COLLECTION

ALSO AVAILABLE IN THE SERIES...

Abba
A great collection of 15 classic Abba hits, including 'Dancing Queen', 'Fernando', 'Take A Chance On Me' and 'Thank You For The Music'.
AM998404

Ballads
A superb collection of 15 well-known ballads, including 'Fix You', 'I Have A Dream', 'Let It Be' and 'What A Wonderful World'.
AM995346

The Beatles
15 classic Beatles hits including 'All My Loving', 'Hey Jude', 'She Loves You' and 'Yellow Submarine'.
NO91322

New Chart Hits
15 top chart hits including 'Cry Me Out', 'Don't Stop Believin'', 'Issues', 'Just Dance' and 'Russian Roulette'.
AM1001077

Classical Favourites
15 classical pieces including 'Jupiter' (Holst), 'Lullaby' (Brahms), 'Minuet In G' (J.S. Bach) and 'Spring' (Vivaldi).
AM998393

Film Songs
15 great film songs including 'Breaking Free', 'Don't Worry, Be Happy', 'Somewhere Out There' and 'You've Got A Friend In Me'.
AM995335

Showtunes
15 great showtunes including 'Any Dream Will Do', 'Circle Of Life', 'Mamma Mia' and 'My Favourite Things'.
AM995324

Today's Hits
15 of today's current chart hits including 'Hallelujah', 'Human', 'If I Were A Boy' and 'Viva La Vida'.
AM998415

...PLUS MANY MORE

Published by
Wise Publications
14-15 Berners Street,
London W1T 3LJ, UK.

Exclusive Distributors:
Music Sales Limited
Distribution Centre, Newmarket Road,
Bury St Edmunds, Suffolk IP33 3YB, UK.
Music Sales Pty Limited
Level 4, Lisgar House, 30-32 Carrington Street,
Sydney, NSW 2000 Australia.

Order No. AM1010471
ISBN 978-1-78305-941-6
This book © Copyright 2015 Wise Publications,
a division of Music Sales Limited.

Edited by Jenni Norey.
Arranged by Chris Hussey.
Music processed by Camden Music Services.

Printed in the EU.

Download to your computer a set of piano accompaniments for this *Huge Chart Hits* edition
(to be played by a teacher/parent).
Visit: **www.hybridpublications.com**
Registration is free and easy.
Your registration code is SS433

Your Guarantee of Quality
As publishers, we strive to produce every book to the highest commercial standards. This book has been carefully designed to minimise awkward page turns and to make playing from it a real pleasure. Particular care has been given to specifying acid-free, neutral-sized paper made from pulps which have not been elemental chlorine bleached. This pulp is from farmed sustainable forests and was produced with special regard for the environment. Throughout, the printing and binding have been planned to ensure a sturdy, attractive publication which should give years of enjoyment. If your copy fails to meet our high standards, please inform us and we will gladly replace it.

www.musicsales.com